Edition Andrés Segovia

Manuel M. Ponce
1882 – 1948

12 Préludes

for Guitar
für Gitarre
pour Guitare

Fingering by / Fingersätze von / Doigtés par
Andrés Segovia

GA 540
ISMN 979-0-001-12775-2

Mainz · London · Berlin · Madrid · New York · Paris · Prague · Tokyo · Toronto
© 1930 SCHOTT MUSIC GmbH & Co. KG, Mainz · © renewed 1958 · Printed in Germany

6 Préludes

Doigtés par A. Segovia

Manuel M. Ponce
1882—1948

I

© 1930 Schott Music GmbH & Co. KG, Mainz · © renewed 1958

II

3

III

IV

5

V

VI

Moderato espressivo

VII

VIII

IX

X

Allegretto expressivo

XI

XII

Schott Music, Mainz 49 960